my first Maze BOOK

ARCTURUS

ARCTURUS

This edition published in 2021 by Arcturus Publishing Limited
26/27 Bickels Yard, 151–153 Bermondsey Street,
London SE1 3HA

Illustrator: Kasia Dudziuk
Designer: Emma Randall
Cover designer: Ms Mousepenny
Writer: Susannah Bailey
Editors: Susannah Bailey, Joe Harris, and Jessica Sinyor

ISBN: 978-1-78950-318-0
CH007019NT
Supplier 33, Date 0921, Print run 12031

Printed in China

RACE TO THE FINISH

Show the fast cars the way to the finish line.

START

FINISH

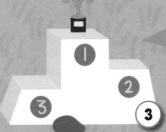

DINOSAUR SWAMP

Guide Timmy the Triceratops back to his family.
Make sure you avoid the other dinos along the way!

START

FINISH

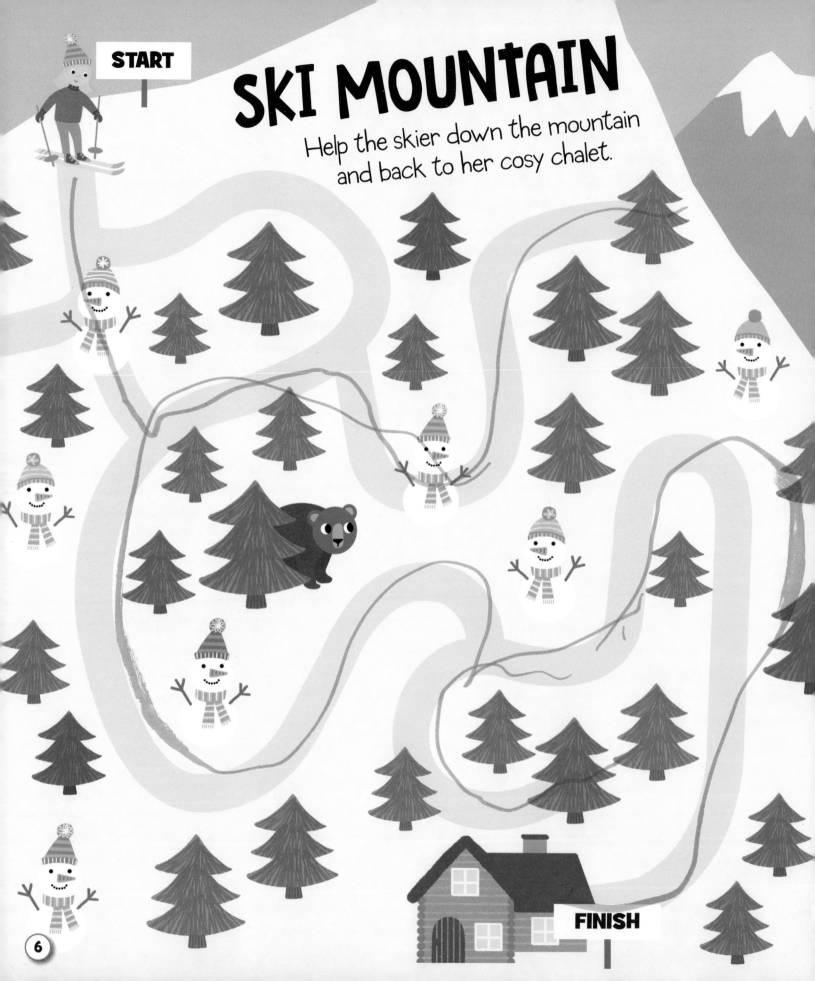

SKI MOUNTAIN

Help the skier down the mountain and back to her cosy chalet.

START

FINISH

6

BIRDS OF A FEATHER

Guide the little pink bird back up to her nest.

FINISH

START

MONKEY PUZZLE

START

Help the little monkey find a clear route through the jungle to meet his friends. Avoid the prickly pineapples!

FINISH

RABBIT WARREN

Lead Barney the bunny through
the tunnels back to his dad.

START

FINISH

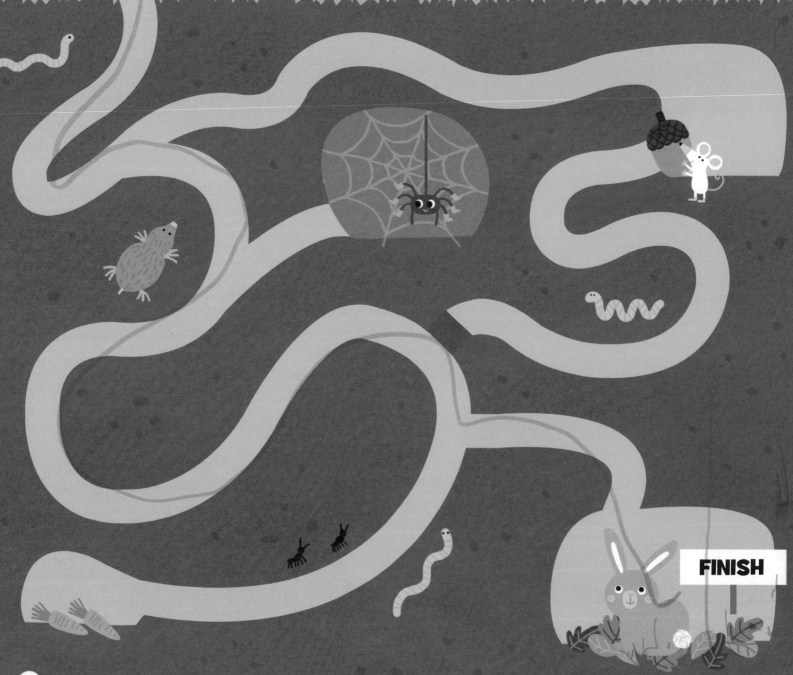

SPACE MISSION

Which way should the rocket go to land safely on the planet?

BALLOON RIDE

Guide the hot-air balloon through the clouds, back to safe ground.

START

FINISH

DEEP-SEA DIVER

Show the diver the path to the treasure.

START

FINISH

BUSY TOWN

START

Drive the car along the road through the town to refuel.

FINISH

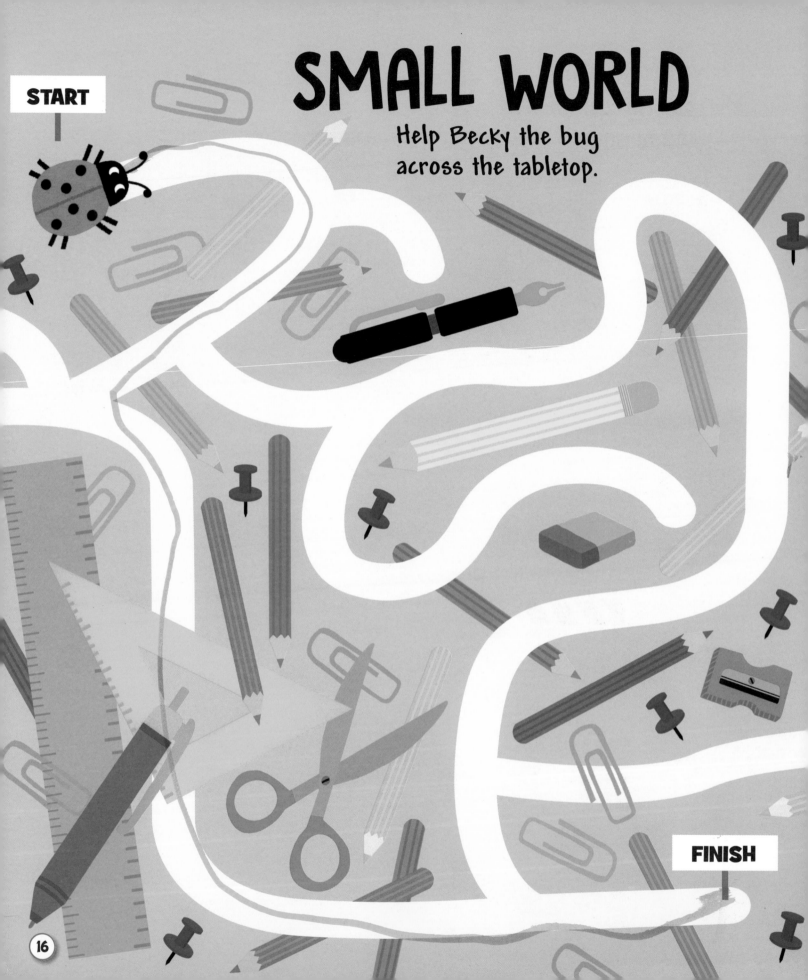

FAIRGROUND

Guide Tom and Tina through the fair so they can ride the Ferris wheel with their friends!

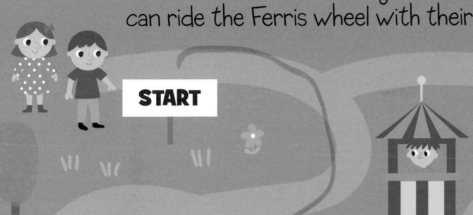

START

FINISH

HAMSTER RUN

Help the hungry hamster reach her food.

START

FINISH

KNIGHT TIME

Show the brave knight the best path through the thorny maze.

START

FINISH

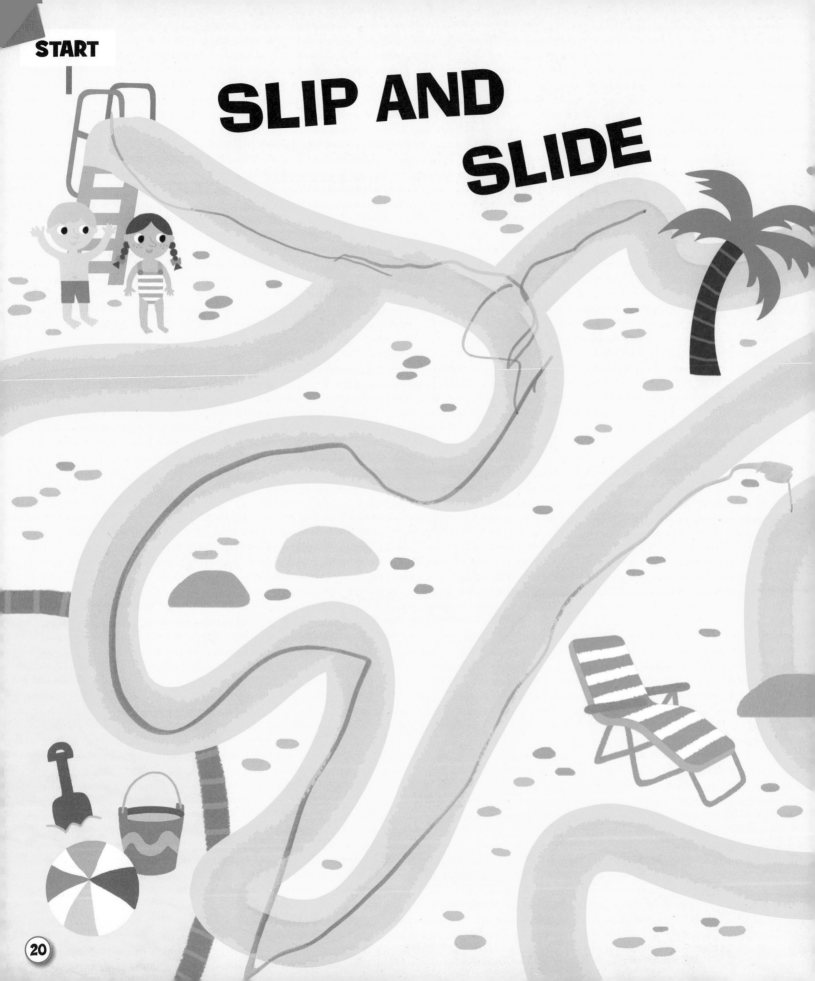

SLIP AND
SLIDE

Guide the children down the super slide to the swimming pool.

FINISH

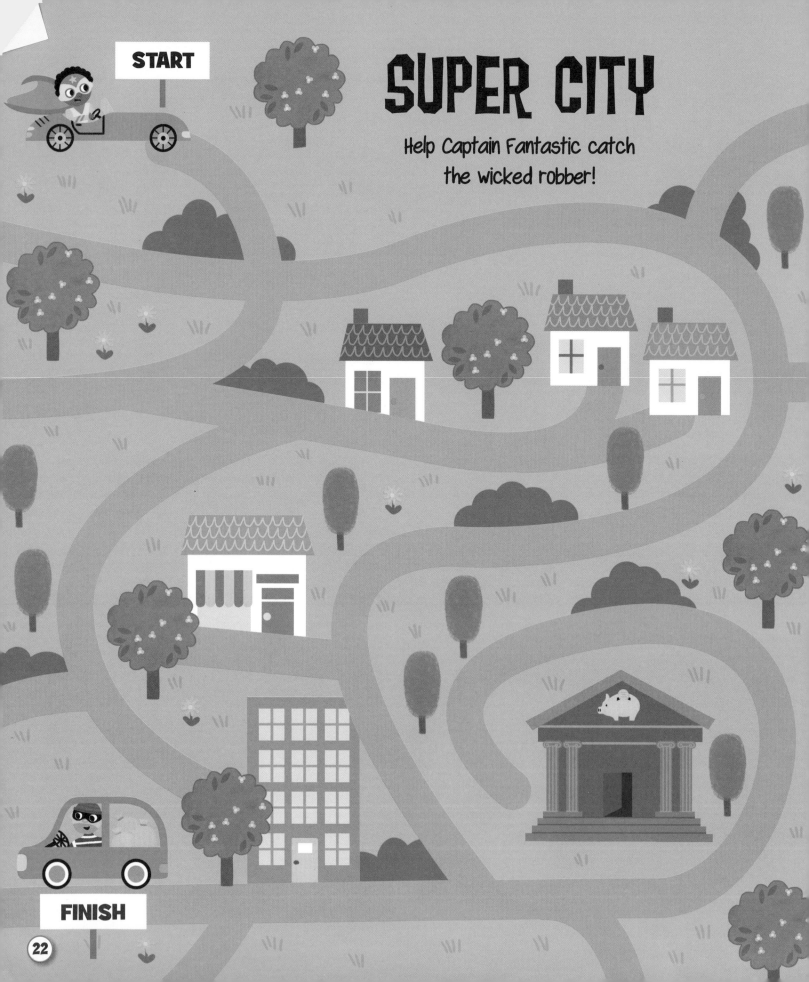

SUPER CITY

Help Captain Fantastic catch
the wicked robber!

START

FINISH

Answers

Race to the Finish
(page 3)

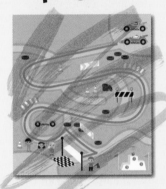

Dinosaur Swamp
(pages 4—5)

Ski Mountain
(page 6)

Birds of a Feather
(page 7)

Monkey Puzzle
(pages 8—9)

Rabbit Warren
(page 10)

Space Mission
(page 11)

Balloon Ride
(page 12)

Deep-Sea Diver
(page 13)

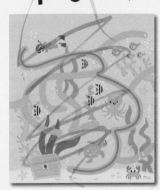

Busy Town
(pages 14—15)

Small World
(page 16)

Fairground
(page 17)

Hamster Run
(page 18)

Knight Time
(page 19)

Slipe and Slide
(pages 20—21)

Super City
(page 22)